"Get in the car," said Dad. "We haven't much time."

"Where are we going?" asked Laura.

"It's a surprise," said Dad. "I'll carry Ben, and you bring the wheelchair."

1

Laura put Ben's wheelchair in the boot of the car
and Dad strapped Ben into the back seat.

"I hope this is a nice surprise," said Ben. "Are
we going to see a film?"

"No. Something better than that," said Dad.

"I know," said Laura. "We're going to the Ice Rink."

"That will be fun for me, won't it?" said Ben. "Can you imagine me with skates on my wheels?"

"It's no good trying to guess," said Dad. "But I promise you'll both be pleased."

Dad drove to the other side of town and stopped the car outside a block of flats.

"This is the place," he said. "Let's get you into your chair, Ben."

"Flats mean stairs," said Ben. "Perhaps you'd better carry me."

Dad carried Ben up the stairs and Laura carried
his wheelchair.

"It's a good job we don't live here," panted
Laura.

"It's an old building," said Ben. "Nobody
thought about wheelchairs when these flats were
built."

Dad rang the bell at one of the flats and a lady
came to the door.

"Come in, come in! I've been expecting you,"
she said. "There are just two left."

"Two what?" asked Ben.

"Wait and see," said Dad. "It's still a surprise."

"I'm sorry about all the stairs," said the lady, looking at Ben's wheelchair. "It's hard enough for me to get up and down them."

"That's O.K.," said Ben. "I'm used to being carried."

The lady led the way into her sitting room. There
was a basket by the fire. In the basket was a cat
and two tiny kittens.

"Kittens!" gasped Laura. "Oh Dad, are we
going to have one?"

"That's the surprise," said Dad. "Take your pick." Ben was delighted. He had wanted a pet for ages.

"I can't decide," he said. "They're both so cuddly."

"Oh Dad!" said Laura. "Can't we have them both?"

In the end, Dad decided to take both kittens. He
said that it would be unkind to separate them.

"You'll have to look after them properly," said
Dad. "Animals aren't toys. You must think of them
as new members of our family."

On the way home, Dad bought the kittens a
basket to sleep in, a rubber mouse and a litter
tray. Ben and Laura helped them to settle in. Ben
called his kitten Lucky, and Laura called hers
Scat.

It was hard work looking after the kittens. Every day Ben and Laura had to feed them and empty their trays. Lucky and Scat were great explorers. They explored every inch of the house, but they were too young to go outside.

"Aren't they funny?" said Laura. "They must be the most mischievous kittens ever."

"Yes," said Ben. "The only time they aren't being naughty is when they're asleep."

"That's rather like you two," smiled Dad.

One Friday evening Dad was going to take Ben
and Laura to stay with their aunt and uncle.

"But we can't leave Lucky and Scat," said
Laura.

"No," said Dad. "They can come too. Auntie
Val and Uncle Keith are looking forward to
meeting them."

When Dad put Ben's wheelchair in the car boot, he left the front door of the house open. He didn't see Lucky slip out into the garden.

"Come on," said Dad. "We're ready. Let's put the kittens in the car."

Scat was asleep in the basket but Lucky was
nowhere to be found. Dad and Laura searched
the house from top to bottom but there was no
sign of him. Ben was trying to be brave but he felt
like crying.

"He must have slipped out when you were loading the car boot, Dad," said Ben. "You've got to find him. Go and see if he's in the garden."

"It's my fault," said Dad. "I should have been more careful. But don't worry, we'll find him."

Dad and Laura searched the front garden and the street but there was no sign of Lucky. Ben was miserable because he couldn't help them.

"It's no good," said Dad. "It's getting dark now. We'll stay here tonight and hope he comes home."

Dad phoned Auntie Val to explain what had happened.

"We could phone the local radio station," said Ben, "and ask them to tell people to look out for him."

"That's a good idea," agreed Dad. "I'll phone them right away. I'm sure somebody will find him."

The next morning the doorbell never stopped
ringing. Everybody had heard the story of Ben's
lost kitten. They brought kittens of all shapes,
sizes and colours but not one of them was Lucky.
Ben was heartbroken.

At lunchtime Dad spoke to Ben.

"I'm very sorry," he said, "but I don't think we're going to find him today. I expect he'll be back in a few days. Somebody will find him."
Ben didn't say anything.

It was time to go to Auntie Val's and Uncle
Keith's. Dad carried Ben to the car and Laura
brought Scat. Scat seemed to be missing his
brother.

"I don't want to go," said Ben. "I want to stay
at home and wait for Lucky."

"We can't do that," said Dad. "Auntie Val and
Uncle Keith are looking forward to seeing us.
Think how upset they would be if we didn't go."

"Think how upset Lucky will be if he comes
home and we're not here," said Ben.

Dad asked the next door neighbours to keep a
look out for Lucky. When they got to Auntie Val's
and Uncle Keith's Ben was still upset.

Auntie Val made a great fuss of Scat which only
made Ben feel worse.

"It doesn't seem right," said Ben. "There
should be two kittens not one. Scat is missing
Lucky as much as I am."

Uncle Keith tried to comfort Ben.

"When I was a boy," he said. "I had a dog named Candy. She ran away once and I thought she had gone forever. I couldn't stop crying." Uncle Keith's story only made Ben cry.

"Don't cry, Ben," he said. "My story has a happy ending. After a week Candy came home."

"But Lucky is only a kitten," sobbed Ben, "and he's never been out of the house before. And if he does come home we won't be there to let him in."

Everybody tried to cheer Ben up. Auntie Val
cooked him his favourite dinner but he couldn't
eat it. Uncle Keith suggested that they all go to
the cinema but Ben didn't want to go.

"This is no good, Ben," said Dad. "Being
unhappy won't bring Lucky back. We'll all go for
a walk in the park. That will make you feel
better."

"I'll go and get his wheelchair," said Laura.
"May I have the keys to the boot?"

Laura went to the car. As she opened the boot she gave a terrific shout. Dad picked up Ben and they all ran outside.

"Whatever is the matter?" asked Auntie Val. "Why did you shout like that?"

"It's Lucky!" laughed Laura. "He was in the boot!"

"What!" said Dad. "He must have jumped in when I was putting in Ben's wheelchair last night."

"He's been in there for hours," said Laura. "He must be starving."

"Oh, Lucky," said Ben. "I'm so glad you're back.
I thought you'd run away for ever."

"I knew we'd find him," said Dad.

"It's lucky I looked in the boot," said Laura.

"It's lucky for Lucky!" said Ben.